Chocolate Cake

CHOCOLATE CAKE

The MIND Method of Weight Control

by
Jakki Wendt

jmp enterprises

2500 clark, burbank, ca 91505   (213) 840-0220

Second Edition

Copyright © 1980 by Delphi Information Sciences Corporation

ISBN 0-930306-12-0

Manufactured in the United States of America

Illustrations by Lyn Mayer
Cover Design by Jill McLemore

To Tom and Amos, my best friends,
who provide me with love
and stability, always . . .

and to those of you who
believe in the power
of your mind.

FOREWORD
BY DR. JOSEPH MURPHY

I recommend this book for its practicality and simplicity. Your subconscious mind is amenable to suggestion and whatever your conscious mind believes, your subconscious will reproduce on the screen of space. Whatever is impressed in the subconscious will always be expressed as form, function, experiences and events. Feed your subconscious with life-giving patterns and your dessert will rejoice and blossom as the rose. Jakki Wendt is to be commended for a brilliant idea and an excellent technique.

Blessings to you,

Dr. Joseph Murphy

CONTENTS

Introduction

I have the key to the Universe! I am going to share it with you. The key is your **mind**; your mind is more powerful than any computer man can or will develop. This key, the **mind**, can provide you with weight loss, as well as health, wealth, success and happiness. **Your mind** is the key to all your desires. You are minutes away from learning how to harness and direct this tremendous energy. The best part is that it's *easy*—it's a "piece of cake."

This book presents the mind method of weight control. It has been so successful that we want to share it with you. Read on and enjoy life as the thin person we know you are!

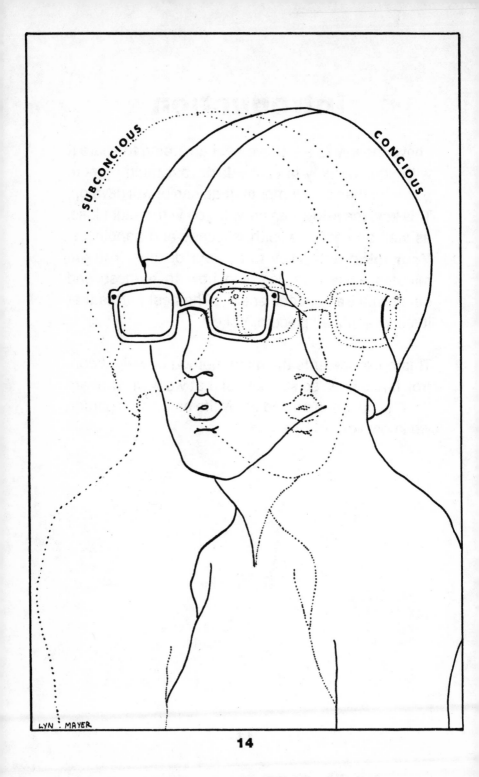

Chocolate Cake

The *Chocolate Cake* method is based on the *mind* method of weight control, with the importance placed on the word *mind*. You have only *one* mind, but it possesses two distinct and individual levels. The **Conscious** mind is the reasoning mind, the one that provides the answer to a mathematical problem or helps you recall how to drive the freeways. The **Subconscious** is the part of the mind that controls breathing, heartbeat and all other involuntary bodily functions in your body while you're asleep. The Subconscious part of your mind is there to protect your existence . . . to keep the body stable and *healthy*. Your Subconscious mind takes its directives from your Conscious mind: from what you *visualize* and just as importantly, from *what you say*. Many of you say, "All I have to do is look at food and I gain weight." Or if one offers you a piece of cake you automatically think "I SHOULDN'T EAT THAT, IT'S FATTENING."

What you think
to yourself
or say out loud
to others,
is actually giving
your subconscious
mind an order.

I visualize the Conscious mind as a computer programmer and the Subconscious mind as the computer. You might enjoy thinking of yourself as the programmer and your Subconscious as your Weight Control Workshop. Your Subconscious mind is always listening, and it always believes exactly what you say. When you say, "I only have to look at food and I gain weight," the Subconscious mind *turns food to fat*. Naturally you say, "But I do gain weight," and this is what we call a belief system.

Belief Systems

Belief systems are the foundations for your Subconscious mind. They are the framework that protects your existence. Belief systems are permanent thoughts in your Subconscious mind that create reality for you.

Negative thoughts about food transform your body into fat.

THESE ARE THE THOUGHTS WE HAVE TO CHANGE. WE HAVE TO CHANGE OUR BASIC SUBCONSCIOUS BELIEF SYSTEMS.

The Conscious Mind is always seeking and selecting data to form your beliefs. To change your body, you must change your beliefs *even in the face of evidence that conflicts*!

This is how you begin to retrain your Subconscious mind. You repeat **"Everything I eat makes me thin and healthy now."** This is called an affirmation—a sentence designed to re-program your Subconscious mind. By repetition, the subconscious accepts, believes and then acts, without judgement, on the command you give it. You must make the affirmation a sing-song in your mind. Say it to yourself when you're in the shower, driving your car, or doodling by yourself. The more often you say the affirmation, the faster the method works.

Here is an example of how it works. If I offer you a piece of chocolate cake you automatically think "Chocolate cake is fattening." That is the belief system you have about chocolate cake. By thinking that thought, *and* eating the cake, you have just issued a command to your subconscious mind to make you fat. Many people believe this information on both the Conscious and Subconscious levels of their mind. To change the Subconscious belief system we eat the cake and continually repeat ***"Everything I eat makes me thin and healthy now!"***

Your Subconscious begins to give your body instructions to make your body thin, even though your Conscious mind *may not accept it as true.*

REMEMBER, YOU ARE DEALING WITH YOUR SUB-CONSCIOUS MIND, YOUR INNER YOU.

This is the place that makes things happen.

As you continue to use the method over a period of time your Subconscious mind begins to determine what foods are healthy for your individual body. Soon you may turn away from chocolate cake and other unhealthy items. You may find yourself craving some foods and rejecting others, even foods you consciously love. *Let this happen. This means the inner you is working. Listen.*

As the method continues and you begin to see weight loss, you will begin to change your belief structure to, *"No food is any more fattening than another."*

You create your own reality! *And* that includes your body! *You* are in control!

Many of our *Chocolate Cake* dieters find a great weight loss immediately, as much as 8-10 pounds in a week. The weight loss is determined by *your belief system.* As you continue to affirm, *"Everything I eat makes me thinner and healthier now!"* your body will begin to tighten up the elasticity. This means no sagging, or wrinkling. The weight loss is started in the areas where it is most needed. Weight may start by redistributing itself, indicated by lost inches and changes in your clothing.

I recommend, after the first reading of the book, that you weigh yourself. After that stay off the scales for 4–6 weeks. Scales are negative programs.

Scales Are Negative Programs

How many times have you dieted and felt really good about the results? With great anticipation you jump on the scale, feeling you must have lost at least 8 pounds. With great expectations you watch the needle, and it shows only 4 or 5 pounds lost. All those days or weeks worth of dieting, and so little loss.

All the goodies passed up . . . the martyred feeling. It seems like the time to *eat*! *And* you binge, wasting your entire effort at dieting! So . . . stay off the scale! Watch your body change. See it in your clothes. Let your friends tell you how great you look, and *agree* with them. *Talk* about your new weight loss method, imagine your clothes being too BIG. Break the vicious diet circle *now*!

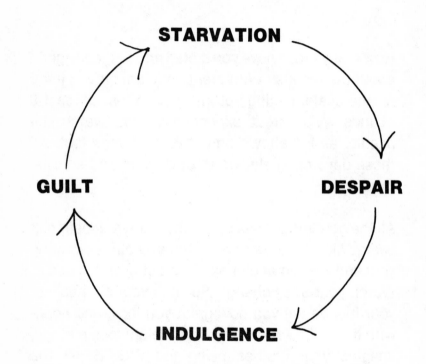

This is the vicious circle diet, one most of us have fallen into at least once. You decide to diet, mostly by deprivation in one form or another. As the long days or weeks of a diet pass, the "poor little me" syndrome begins, and you feel despair. The dieting hasn't paid off, and you become depressed and irritable. You say to yourself, "I'm tired of this I deserve a goodie." The one goodie turns to many and guilt is started. "Why did I ever eat that? I've ruined my diet." And off you go into starvation again.

With the Chocolate Cake method of weight loss, life can be fun again. Eat everything, anywhere, anytime, use your *mind* to remove the guilt about eating.

Remember there are only *three* things you have to do to lose weight:

EAT 6–8 TIMES A DAY

DRINK 64 OUNCES OF WATER A DAY

say: EVERYTHING I EAT MAKES ME THINNER AND HEALTHIER *NOW!*

It's easy! It's fun! **Life should be fun.** *Each day is a new beginning.*

Negative Programming

We remember mother saying "Don't eat that, you'll get fat." Or, we remember the feelings of guilt when we took a cookie from the cupboard knowing that mother would tell us that it would "ruin your appetite" or that it would "make you fat." Mother also used dirty looks on countless occasions as a reminder of her repeated warning. With every bite of food we took, the memory of her words sent the message to our subconscious that "what you are eating is making you fat."

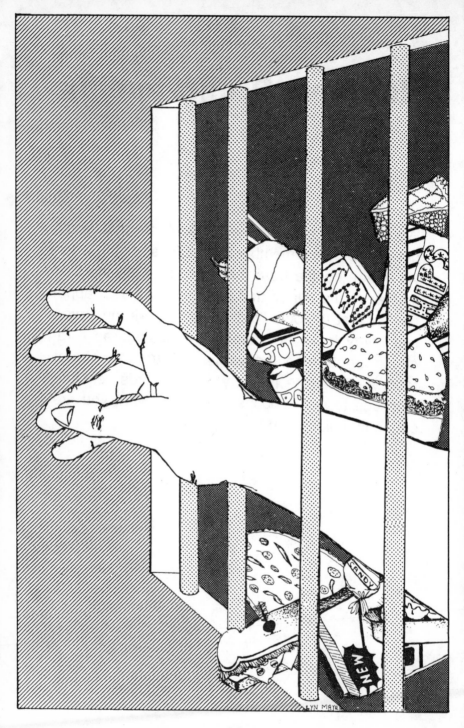

This is a belief system that food = fat, and we call that belief system, a negative program. Reinforcement by friends that they too had received the same warnings about food from their mothers, reminded us that we could not eat pizza because *Mother* told us that it was fattening. Or we disregarded Mother's warning, and feeling guilty, ate as if it were our last meal.

While enjoying our food, we reminded ourselves that although what we were eating was fattening, we promised ourselves that tomorrow we would diet to lose the pounds we gained today.

Most dieters **don't eat**. At most, they may eat one meal a day and that's dinner. What happens then? The Subconscious says, "This person is starving me." So to maintain your existence the Conscious mind sends the "fat" signals to the Subconscious with every biteful of food you eat. As a result your body stores fat to use when you **don't eat**, as in crash diets or periodic starvation.

Think about this for a moment, how do we feed babies? We feed them every 2-3 hours all day and into the night! The baby's system is functioning efficiently, working constantly. As the baby grows up he still wants to eat all day long, but as busy adults we try to force a child to conform to our habits. When the child has snacked all day long, he is not very hungry at dinnertime and we become upset. "He's not eating dinner" we say, and we begin to force him into the three-meal-a-day eating habit . . . getting him organized for the outside world. That's when the guilt about food starts. As the child continues to grow, we begin to watch how much he eats at each meal and warn him about the *dangers* of food. Calories, nutrients, and *fat*! Eating becomes a pleasure-guilt process. As an adult we fight this guilt by *not* eating!

GO BACK TO CHILDLIKE EATING HABITS!
EAT 6–8 TIMES A DAY!

Your body is like a machine, it needs fuel to burn fat and run efficiently.

After digestion, your system becomes sluggish and stagnant. Keep it running.

Don't be afraid to eat!

This is a new method for your mind and body. It's normal to be skeptical and afraid of gaining more weight. Remember we've been trained to believe that *food* does bad things to our body, not that our *MIND* does bad things to our body. But eat anyway and say the affirmation, ***"Everything I eat makes me thinner and healthier now!"***

So, in order to avoid the storing of fat cells you must **eat 6–8 times a day**. What size meals? Any size that fits into *your* routine or lifestyle, but don't skip meals or snacks. Avoid a coffee and orange juice breakfast; eat something solid: toast, fruit, a four course breakfast . . . whatever fits your routine, *but eat!* Eat something every 2–3 hours. Your body is like a machine it runs more efficiently when its kept moving. It is necessary to eat 6–8 times a day to insure that fat cells do not accumulate. Say the affirmation with every snack and meal.

**You are teaching your mind
not to store unneeded substances.**

Most dieters don't drink water; they drink coffee and diet sodas but not pure, fresh water. As with food, our Subconscious mind wants to protect us against dehydration, so water retention results.

Drink 64 ounces of water daily. Your body will flush the water through and push the old water out. The water rinses away the residue of all the food you've eaten. Water is also wonderful for your skin and complexion.

Don't drink all the water at once! We don't want you to slosh around! Drink one glass of water 15 to 20 minutes before each meal or snack. By bedtime you will have had eight meals and eight glasses of water. Going to the bathroom alot? *Good!!* It's working.

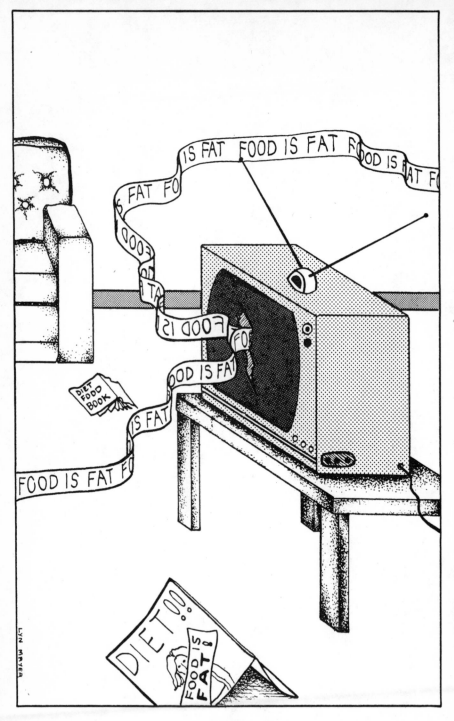

Examples of Negative Programming can be found in all aspects of our lives. This means you have consciously programmed yourself with thoughts of "food = fat." You have undoubtedly indulged in crash diets or other methods. All of these methods reinforce the Negative Programming of your Subconscious.

LYN MAYER

44

Diet Pills!! When you're told that a pill will reduce your appetite and speed up weight loss, generally, you do experience loss of appetite and weight. But what happens when you reach your weight goal and discontinue the pills? Suddenly, you find that although you are eating no more than you did when you were taking the medication you begin to regain. Why? The belief system was that the **medication** would *make* you lose weight. You *trained* your Subconscious to make your body thin by use of the pills. *Your Subconscious actually did the work!!*

Once you stop your medication you fail to reinforce your Subconscious with the positive programming it came to expect. Soon the negative thoughts return because the belief system of diet pills is gone. Once again foods equals fat, and the Subconscious follows your orders to make your body fat with each mouthful of food that you eat.

At this point, you usually force yourself into another dieting method which creates an uneven metabolism.

Metabolism governs the rate at which your body uses food to generate energy.

Your *mind* governs your metabolism!

The affirmation is designed to make your metabolism run at its peak, therefore it is absolutely necessary to eat

6–8 times a day

to insure that your metabolism runs constantly. It is the number of times you eat in a day, *not* the quantity that matters. On the other hand, the less frequently you eat, the *slower* your metabolism becomes, and your body begins to store fat cells and water for periods of starvation.

Don't be afraid to eat eight times a day. And don't be afraid to eat just before bedtime; your body works during the night anyway. For an example if you stop eating at eight o'clock in the evening and you don't eat breakfast until eight o'clock in the morning, you have gone 12 hours *without food!* Fat cells may begin to form again, and your blood sugar level may drop. *What happens then?* You wake up in the morning craving something sweet for breakfast. So, banish your fear of weight gain by eating.

LYN MAYER

If you don't eat frequently, when you do partake of food, your Subconscious mind, now programmed for periodic starvation, stores more food as fat cells. This storage is a necessary part of your body's existence, **only** when you are not eating. That's why you *must* eat 6-8 times a day. **Avoid** starvation and avoid the storing of fat cells! Your body will also have excess storage of fluid if you have withheld proper amounts of water. Frequent watering of your body prevents storage of fluids in anticipation of dehydration.

PROPER AMOUNTS OF WATER ARE **AT LEAST 8** GLASSES A DAY. THIS HELPS ELIMINATE THE BODY'S NEED TO STORE WATER. WATER FLUSHES OUT THE OLD YOU!

food ≈ thin

There is always someone we know who is enviably thin in spite of their large appetite. Such people believe that no matter what they eat, they will not gain weight. They usually list all the foods eaten the last 24 hours and when asked if they have gained weight after all this indulgence, the response is "Oh, no! No matter how much I eat, I never gain weight. As a matter of fact, sometimes I eat like a horse and lose weight."

You must question their belief system. Their belief system will come as no surprise. Their thoughts when eating are focused only on the nutritious values of the food as well as the energy the body is deriving from the meal.

The belief system we uncover is "Think Thin, Be Thin." *Be thin* and *healthy now!*

"If it is as simple as all that," you ask, "why doesn't everyone do it?" That is a good question. Certainly there are many of you who have never heard of a belief system. And even if you have thought about the theory, you did not understand positive and negative programming and its influence upon the *mind*. Of course, there are always some who, out of guilt, do not feel that they deserve to be thin, or who think they really enjoy being fat. For those people, this plan, unlike all other methods, will enable them to easily make that decision by merely changing their attitudes and belief systems. If you do want to be thin and shed fat for the rest of your life, all that you need to do is follow our instructions on how to reconstruct your Subconscious. Start today! You have nothing to *lose* but *pounds* and all the beauty of *life* to *gain*.

58

Bodycontrol is based on a simple method of repro-gramming your Subconscious mind with respect to food. We no longer affirm that "food equals fat" but that food, any and **all** food, is making us **thin** *and* **healthy** *now*. This is, in fact, a simple reprogram-ming of the data stored in your computer, **your Sub-conscious mind**. Your Subconscious, your Weight Control Workshop, receives and stores in a memory bank all the data it receives from your Conscious mind. Like a computer, it does not judge whether the data is true or false, good or bad, correct or in-correct. Ever since birth, your computer has been constantly programmed by yourself, as well as by the data fed to you by parents, teachers, friends and the media. Everytime you heard a warning about a certain food being fattening, you consciously chose to take the warning seriously and store it as data in your computer, or you chose to disregard the data. If you have a severe weight problem, you obviously have programmed your computer with a tremendous amount of "food equals fat" data. In turn, if you have no problem with your weight, your weight control workshop has been fed with a lot of "food equals thin" data concerning food.

Just as a computer can be reprogrammed, you can feed new data into your Subconscious. Each time you think of food, partake of food, or discuss food with anyone, you can choose to enter either negative or positive data into your computer. Decide today that henceforth all food information will be **positive**. With each positive thought you feed into your Subconscious, take the negative out. We suggest that you begin positive programming by simply affirming, in your Conscious mind while you eat, that **"Everything I eat makes me thinner and healthier** *NOW.***"** These words are chosen very carefully. **Thin** is used because you no longer want to associate food as fat. **Healthy** is used to confirm the fact that your body will take enough food to keep you in good health. The word **now** is an order to your Subconscious to start the reprogramming IMMEDIATELY to carry out your *Thin* and *Healthy* command at once.

Because your Subconscious mind takes everything you say literally and acts accordingly, we know that it is beneficial for you to affirm with every meal and snack—and *as often as possible*—that **"Everything I eat makes me thin and healthy now."**

While lying in your bath tub, passing a mirror, or daydreaming, repeat "I am thin and healthy now!" *The more often you make this affirmation the easier your subconscious makes the change and the faster the weight loss occurs.*

Acknowledging that it has taken years to negatively program your mind, you can understand that your reprogramming process will also take some time. Happily, though, you can feed the new data into your Subconscious at a rate as fast as you desire. With each food you eat—for instance, chocolate cake—affirm that it is making you **thin and healthy now**. Visualize changing the program entitled "Chocolate cake equals fat" and replacing it with your new program labeled "Chocolate cake is making me **thin and healthy now**!" Remember that your Subconscious is unable to make a value judgement of whether this information is true or false, so it will not say to you, "Oh, come on, you must be joking." It will take the information fed to it through your Conscious mind and act accordingly.

As you eat the cake, affirm your new positive belief by relating to yourself and others that it is making you **"Thin and Healthy *now.*"** Imagine that all excess nutrients from the cake will be carried into your elimination system. Everytime you get a negative program on a particular food, like "bananas are fattening" change the program to "bananas are making me thin and healthy *now.*" As the transformation is completed, you will be a normal eater.

You need only eat 6-8 times a day and drink 64 ounces of water. Begin to reprogram and affirm that **"Everything I eat makes me thinner and healthier *now!*"** Once the program is firmly implanted in your subconscious mind and it becomes your new belief system and foundation, *then*, you no longer have to give it a conscious thought.

Remember your three "Must Do's":

1.
You must eat
6–8 times
a day.

2.

**You must drink
at least
64 oz. of water
a day . . . 8 full glasses.**

3.

You MUST make the
affirmation
"Everything I eat
makes me thinner
and healthier now."
as often as possible
during each meal
or it won't work.
Then eat all you want.

Everything I eat
makes me
thinner & healthier
NOW!

70

THE AFFIRMATION CARD

At the back of the book you will find weight reduction affirmation cards. These cards are to be placed in front of you at each meal and every snack. Use the card in restaurants, home, and work—anywhere you eat. Make sure it sits in front of you as often as possible, even when you're *not* eating. Place it on your desk at work and in front of you at home. The more often you see the affirmation, the faster it works to re-program your subconscious mind. This card is designed to trigger your subconscious mind *even if your conscious mind is not paying attention*. Carry it with you, relax and have fun.

SPOTS IN FRONT OF YOUR EYES

You have seen the "peel-and-stick" colored adhesive dots. Buy a small package of them in a color that will show up, like a bright red or blue. Get the *small* ones. Place one of these dots on each of your bathroom mirrors, on your kitchen cabinets, your refrigerator, on the face of your watch, the windshield of your car, your telephone. Place them everywhere at work and home.

The first week *look* at the dot and think the affirmation in your mind. Think, **"Everything I eat makes me thinner and healthier *now*!"** Soon, with no conscious mental effort, the dots will automatically trigger your subconscious mind.

If you have another goal, use a second dot of another color. Say the affirmation in your mind each time you see either dot. Don't try more than two at a time. When you reach one goal, try another.

74

CHOCOLATE CAKE—MIND METHOD—AS A WAY OF LIFE

There you have it. We have presented to you the fastest and easiest way to lose and *maintain* your weight.

The best part of the MIND method is the wonderful joy of living a normal lifestyle. Business luncheons, dinner dates, birthday parties, wedding receptions, parties and vacations are yours to enjoy. All the forbiddens are now yours. Remember **"Everything I eat makes me *thin* and *healthy* now!"** and you will become the thin person we know you are.

Thoughts to Remember

1. You make choices. Choose to be **Thin and Healthy** *now*.

2. You MUST eat 6–8 times a day and drink at least 8 glasses of water a day.

3. Affirm "I am *thin* and *healthy now*" at every opportunity.

4. Your mind is a computer. Your Subconscious makes no value judgements. Feed in the positive program. Destroy the negative program.

5. Break the vicious circle *now*.

6. Enjoy eating. It is a natural sense, like feeling a fine fabric or seeing a beautiful painting.

7. Rejoice at the knowledge given to you. Be grateful for a lifetime of easy weight control.

8. Share this knowledge with your friends. Turn them on to a lifetime of happiness with no more fear, no more dieting.

9. Believe in the power of your Subconscious mind. You will reap unbelievable results.

10. Never let this plan slip away from you. Reread parts of your book every day.

11. Using this plan, you join the ranks of "normal" eaters. **Congratulations!**

Questions and Answers About Chocolate Cake

1. Is this a joke, can it really work?

No, this is not a joke, it really works! This method deals directly with the subconscious mind where *you* control your own reality. *You are in control!* This method is the most fun and easiest of any I know to lose weight and maintain the loss for the rest of your life. With this method, you release the guilt of eating and enjoy life.

2. I am skeptical of this method and fearful of gaining more weight.

In the beginning, it's normal to be afraid of this method; it's new to you. It works by repetitiously retraining your thinking process. It may take time, based on the strength of your old beliefs, but it works.

Everything I eat
makes me
thinner & healthier
NOW!

3. What about calories and nutrients?

I believe your *mind* controls your body. The body worked long before science came along and put labels on how the body works. It is your belief system about food that makes you gain or lose weight, not food, calories or nutrients.

4. How much weight can I lose?

The amount of weight you lose depends on you; the more consistent you are with the program the faster it works. Say the affirmation as often as possible, with each *bite* when you're alone. Follow the three-part program. Five to ten pounds a week is possible if you use self-honesty in your habits.

Everything I eat
makes me
thinner & healthier
NOW!

5. *Can I gain weight on Chocolate Cake?*

No, not if you follow the three parts: drink 64 ounces of water, eat 6–8 times a day, and say the affirmation as often as possible. *Be patient.* If you change your diet it may take longer for the process to work. For an example, if you have never allowed yourself to have desserts, and on the *Chocolate Cake* method you now begin to eat cakes, donuts, ice cream and sugar-type products, your body needs time to re-adjust to the new foods and the new program. If, however, you do not change your basic diet but just add the chocolate cake method, your weight loss will be immediate.

6. *Can I eat anything?*

Yes. I really mean anything; *not* just proper diet foods, but anything you'd like to have. By letting yourself have anything, you may lose the obsession for that item. You do not feel deprived or suffer from despair. Eat, enjoy, and lose weight.

Everything I eat
makes me
thinner & healthier
NOW!

7. Should I eat smaller amounts?

No, but make sure you eat *6–8 times* a day. Eat something even when you're not hungry. Remember, the purpose of these many meals or snacks is to keep your metabolism running. You will get to the point where you don't want to eat. *Eat a small something anyway.* An orange, apple, nuts, *but something. Don't skip any of the feeding times.*

8. I hate water. Do I have to drink eight glasses?

Yes, the method depends on all three parts to work. That is: eating 6–8 times a day, drinking all the water, and saying the affirmation. The water can be consumed hot or cold; try flavoring it with a slice of lemon. *Remember, coffee, alcohol, juices and sodas do not count as water.* The point of the water is to flush out the old water in your system to keep your body watered so it will not retain water, and to keep your elimination system working, *not to fill you up.* Drink the water throughout your day; drinking a glass 20 minutes before each meal and snack throughout the day will be certain to use all the water before bedtime.

Everything I eat
makes me
thinner & healthier
NOW!

9. People laugh when I tell them about my new Chocolate Cake *weight loss method.*

Don't pay any attention. The *Chocolate Cake* method is unique and simple, and it does work. In our society, we are not used to using even ten percent of our minds and we have been programmed negatively from birth. We can only show people that it works. We can show them that diet, and life in general, can be easy and fun.

10. I work, how can I eat that often?

Carry individually wrapped nuts, raisins, apples, cookies, or bananas. These items can count as a meal or snack. Find a plastic juice container, and fill it with water. Explain to the people around you that you *have* to eat. Carry enough to share, and you'll find you can eat anywhere, anytime.

Everything I eat
makes me
thinner & healthier
NOW!

11. Should I exercise?

That's up to you, I suggest yoga for stretching muscles. If you like doing exercise, then by all means do, but the *Chocolate Cake* method does not require exercise.

12. I go to the bathroom more frequently.

Good, this method uses your system more efficiently. This means your elimination system is working to release what you have eaten, and the water is flushing it through. You may find, if you have suffered from constipation in the past, that the *Chocolate Cake* method helps to eliminate that problem.

Everything I eat
makes me
thinner & healthier
NOW!

13. My clothes are getting bigger!

Great, its working!

14. What if I need help?

Call or write to me. An address and telephone hot-line number is listed in the back of the book. I love hearing from people. Let me know of any problems you may have *and* the good news you have.

```
Everything I eat
makes me
thinner & healthier
NOW!
```

CAN YOU TEACH AN OLD DOG NEW TRICKS? A FOOTNOTE

Can you teach an old dog new tricks? *Yes.* We can all learn anything we put our minds to. *We* control our rate of learning, or re-learning, and memory.

Remember, the *Chocolate Cake* method is **unique**. You are untrained in the positive, aggressive use of your mind. You have been told over and over about the effects of calories, nutrients, and exercise on your body.

THESE ARE MYTHS!

Man's body was designed a long time before Science came along to describe and give a name to how the body functions. Man was designed to *move mountains with his mind*, but with technology he forgot.

You have accepted the views of your family and society on food. Those beliefs have made you like you are. For *now*, the negative beliefs—fear about weight gain, and guilt about food—are the stronger emotions. They have more influence over your subconscious mind than your new affirmation. Change that by repeating **"Everything I eat makes me thinner and healthier *now!*"**

Be patient. The more entrenched your old belief system is . . . *the longer it may take.*

But hang in there. It works for everyone with a mind.

Everyone is capable of changing belief systems. *But* change is difficult when your system is paralyzed with *fear.* Your conscious mind fears change; it doesn't want to lose control.

EAT AND RELAX!

Release your fear. *Chocolate Cake* works. Be honest with yourself; follow the method exactly

OR IT WON'T WORK!

Eat *6–8 times a day.*

DON'T
SKIP
ANY!

Drink eight glasses of water daily. (64 ounces)

YES,
ALL 8
GLASSES

Say the affirmation **"Everything I eat makes me thinner and healthier *now*,"** as often as possible during eating times—with each bite if you are eating alone.

Yes, an old dog can learn new tricks.

Exercise

Many times I'm asked how I feel about exercise. Personally, I don't like vigorous, sweaty exercise. I don't mind doing activities by myself, *but not* jogging or running. Companionship doesn't make those activities any easier for me. I agree that exercise is necessary, the muscles in the human body require exercise or movement, and the older the body gets the more exercise it needs. Now when I talk about exercise I'm talking about *stretching* muscles. Many forms of exercise do not touch every muscle and organ of the body. If you say that the objective of exercise is to get your heart to pump, then even yoga does that.

I feel *yoga* is the perfect and only exercise necessary for the maintenance of the human body. Yoga is a blend of body and mind. As you do yoga, you use the visualization techniques to command your body. The advantages to yoga are immense; it can be done alone or in groups, in bad weather or good, and in a small amount of space. *Mindless* exercise, in any form, is a waste of time and energy. No matter what form of exercise you decide to do, *think* about what it does for your body.

Affirmation Cards

Everything I eat
makes me
thinner & healthier
NOW!

¡MON
thinner & healthier
makes me
Everything I eat

Set in front of your meal plate

Cut out this page and fold
as illustrated above.

Everything I eat
makes me
thinner & healthier
NOW!

Set in front of your meal plate

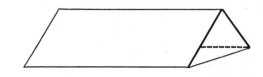

Cut out this page and fold
as illustrated above.

Everything I eat
makes me
thinner & healthier
NOW!

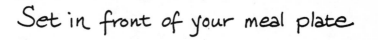

Set in front of your meal plate

Cut out this page and fold
as illustrated above.

Everything I eat
makes me
thinner & healthier
NOW!

Everything I eat
makes me
thinner & healthier
NOW!

Everything I eat
makes me
thinner & healthier
NOW!

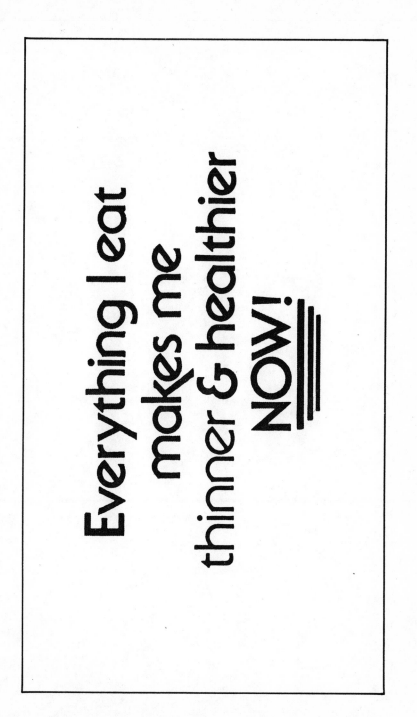

Everything I eat
makes me
thinner & healthier
NOW!

Posters

8½ × 11-inch posters of each illustration are
available from the publisher.

$5.00 each
3 for $10.00
4 or more $3.00 each

Printed on heavy-duty, high-quality paper.

Send your check to:

Delphi Information Sciences Corporation
1416–6th Street
Santa Monica, CA 90401

Satisfaction Guaranteed or your money returned.

Chocolate Cake Hotline

Hotline Number:

(213) 845-9668 for
questions or problems
regarding the method

Chocolate Cake
Cassette

Use the coupon below for **Chocolate Cake Training Cassette** at $5.00

Group seminars in your home or neighborhood for 10 or more people. Rates available. Call Hotline for information.

JMP
2500 Clark B
Burbank, Calif. 91505

Please put my name on your mailing list to receive publishing information.

Check enclosed (   ).

Name _____

Address _____

City, State, ZIP _____
